A PENNY MAGAZINE SPECIAL

JAMES CROLL

and his Adventures in Climate and Time

James Croll
1821 - 1890

First published in 2021 by

Design & typesetting by Madwolf Design
www.madwolf.co.uk

Printed in the UK by Charlesworth Press
Printed using paper from well managed forests

British Library Cataloguing in Publication Data
A catalogue record for this book is available from the British Library

ISBN 978-0-9556968-5-5

Published for

Royal Scottish Geographical Society www.rsgs.org

Lord John Murray House 15-19 North Port Perth PH1 5LU
Charity SC015599

A PENNY MAGAZINE SPECIAL

JAMES CROLL

and his Adventures in Climate and Time

Written by
Jo Woolf

Illustrated by
Dylan Gibson

EDITOR'S LETTER

"The mind is not a vessel to be filled,
but rather a fire to be kindled…"

(Plutarch)

James Croll was a young man who fell in love with learning through a popular magazine he stumbled across in a shop window. Despite being unfortunate in his health and coming from a poor background, and having to try many different jobs, he eventually found one that suited him. This job was perfect because it gave him the time, head space and access he needed to thrive. As a result, he was able to spend more of his time exploring some of the most important scientific questions of his day.

He exchanged ideas with many leading scientists, and contributed enormously to our understanding of ice ages. He explained how many ice ages had occurred and that they were predictable in the future, but at a time when science was still debating a single ice age. He was truly one of the world's first 'climate scientists' and although his legacy is not well known, his was a fundamental plank of long-term climate science.

To celebrate the bicentenary of James Croll's birth, we want to share his story. We hope to inspire you all with this story of success despite hardship. To enthuse you with his story of achievement and persistence. And to encourage you to explore and learn, so that you might in turn stumble over that topic, idea or subject that fires your own intellect and fills your own life with the joy of learning.

Mike Robinson
Chief Executive of the Royal Scottish Geographical Society
January 2021

Ladies, gentlemen and children... welcome!

My name is Croll. James Croll. I am truly humbled and honoured to be here with you today.

Do you see all these wonderful people in the audience? They call me a brilliant scientist, and they have come to hear me speak about some of the biggest questions in the universe. How was the Earth made, what caused the ice ages, how old is the Sun, what makes the ocean currents flow? These are the things that have fascinated me all my life.

If you'd known me when I was a child, you would never have guessed that I'd be here today. Between you and me, I'm amazed that I've even lived this long. I want to share my story with you. I'm going to show you how my passion for knowledge began, and what made me start asking the questions that nobody could answer...

3

I was born on a cold snowy night in January 1821. My mother and father lived in a hamlet called Little Whitefield in Perthshire. They were tenant farmers, meaning that they didn't own their land but they were allowed to farm it. Several generations of my family had lived there before us; they used to spell their name Croil or Croyl. To bring in some extra money, my father also worked as a stonemason. All our neighbours respected him: he was thoughtful and gentle, but he had a tendency to worry about things unnecessarily. My mother, on the other hand, was blessed with plenty of common sense. With all the problems that were coming our way, she needed every bit of it!

I was three years old when disaster struck our family. We were told that we had to leave our home. The landlord, who owned it, wanted to take back the house and the land so that he could make a bigger farm for himself. Although he gave us a smaller plot of land not far away, it made life very difficult for us. Now, we only had a couple of acres and the land was very poor for growing crops or feeding livestock. Sometimes there was barely enough food to go around, and my father had to travel further afield in order to earn enough money.

Normally I would have started going to school when I was about five years old. But my parents decided that this was too early, and so I was allowed a few more years of freedom to enjoy myself! I can't say I minded at all. Meanwhile, my parents and my older brother, Alexander, taught me to read and write. The local schoolmaster would drop by to give me some lessons, too.

There was another reason why I didn't start school earlier. For some unknown reason, I started to have pains in my head, and these got really bad unless I kept my cap on at all times, even indoors. Lots of people wore caps in those days, but no one wore them indoors! I felt very embarrassed and self-conscious. I was horrified at the idea of having to sit in a school classroom with my cap on, because all the other children would laugh at me.

Finally, when I was nine years old, I started attending school in the nearby village of Guildtown. It was two miles away, and I had to walk there and back every day. Some of our teachers were nice, but others were horrible and we were afraid of them! I was never very good at reading or spelling. My teachers called me a 'dull scholar', and I got very bored in class. I learned how to escape, though: I started daydreaming. I could float away in my own thoughts, and it made me very happy. Daydreaming became a lifelong habit!

A few years later I had to leave school so that I could help my mother at home. I was sad, because I missed seeing my friends and by that time I was enjoying my lessons. But my brother Alexander had died when he was 10, and my youngest brother, William, had died in infancy, leaving only myself and another brother, David, who was hunchbacked. My father was still working away, so I had to look after our cows and do some chores around the house.

I thought that my days of learning were over. But how wrong I was! One day, when I had gone to visit the market in Perth, I was looking around the town and happened to glance in a bookshop window. What I saw changed my life. There on display was the first edition of the Penny Magazine, published by the Society for the Diffusion of Useful Knowledge. It looked amazing. I'd never seen anything like it before! On impulse, I went in and bought a copy.

I was overjoyed, because it contained so much interesting information about all kinds of things - the natural world, the seasons and the weather, the night sky, important events in history, and famous people. I read it and re-read it loads of times, and couldn't wait for the next issue.

Now I had plenty of things to think about - interesting subjects, like nature and history, the Earth and the universe. I would ask myself things like, what if the stars and planets didn't exist? I decided that there would just be space. But then I wondered, what if space didn't exist? What would be left? I spent ages thinking about it, but I couldn't answer that question at all!

The Penny Magazine gave me such an appetite for learning that I wished I had more books to read. Unfortunately, we had very few books in the house, so whenever I was given a few pennies I saved them up until I could buy some books for myself. My parents thought this was rather strange at first, but they soon got used to me burying my head in the latest edition on science or philosophy.

Before long, I was old enough to start earning some money myself. I didn't really want to do this: I would much rather have gone to university and carried on learning! But it would have cost a lot of money, and we were far too poor to think of such a thing. I had to contribute towards the cost of running the farm, paying our rent and buying food. So I became an apprentice millwright. This means that I was learning the skills from an experienced millwright, who was my boss.

Together, we travelled around Scotland, repairing and servicing all kinds of mills - sawmills that cut wood for timber, threshing mills that separate the grain from the chaff, and corn mills that grind up the grain for flour. I thought I would enjoy it, but it was a big mistake! I knew all about the theories of mechanics, but mending machines was hard physical work. We didn't earn very much and we had to sleep in all kinds of uncomfortable places, such as barns and stables, often with rats crawling around us. What annoyed me most was that I was too tired to do any daydreaming!

I decided that being a millwright didn't suit me at all. I came home again, and because I had some time on my hands in the winter I went back to the local school to study algebra. Who wants to study algebra, I hear you ask? Well, I did. I thought it was fascinating! Admittedly, at 22 I was far older and bigger than all the other children in the class... but they didn't seem to mind that much...

Then in spring, when the fine weather returned, I got myself a job as a joiner. I loved the work, and I was quite good at it as well. I helped to build a new church in Kinrossie.

When it was finished, I travelled down to Glasgow and found more work. It was a happy time - but a few years later, I started to have a lot of pain in my elbow. I'd had a problem with this joint ever since I was a young lad, but now the problem was getting worse. The doctor told me that the work I was doing was putting far too much strain on it, and he advised me to find a more leisurely occupation. I was really sad, but I didn't have much choice. I tried to think of other things I could do.

What should I do next? It was a question that puzzled me for a long time. I had to find a job that didn't involve too much physical effort, while earning enough money to pay my bills.   I wasn't trained as a clerk, and I wasn't qualified as a teacher. Yet I was interested in so many things - astronomy, pneumatics, hydrostatics, light, heat, electricity, magnetism, and the laws of motion. Ideally, I would love to have spent all my days just studying and thinking, but nobody was going to pay me to do that!

One day I had a bright idea. I was wandering across the bridge in Perth when someone thrust an advertising leaflet into my hand. A new shop was opening, selling tea and coffee. Immediately, I went along to ask if I could have a job. The owner offered to set me up in business, and he became a good friend. A few months later I moved to Elgin in Aberdeenshire and opened my own tea shop.

I had lots of customers, although sometimes I made rather a mess of things... it was quite tricky parcelling up little packets of tea with my stiff joints and awkward fingers! But on the plus side, I had plenty of time for my studies!

One of the happiest events in my whole life happened while I was living in Elgin. I met a young woman called Isabella MacDonald, and we fell in love. I knew that Isabella would be my perfect partner: she was kind and gentle, and always asked me what I was reading. We took long country walks together and I explained to her all about the Earth, the Moon and the stars. I told her that I could see a simple beauty in the laws of science, and I could sense a deeper truth that somehow binds them all together.

Isabella and I decided to embark on a new venture. One of our friends had just finished building a new hotel in Blairgowrie, and he was looking for a married couple to be the proprietors. He assured us that we were the ideal candidates for the role! I thought I would save money and make all the furniture myself, so with my carpentry skills I set about making dozens of chairs, tables and bedsteads.

We looked forward to welcoming our first guests, but sadly, we had very few visitors. Looking back, I admit that we should have considered the prospects more carefully. Blairgowrie already had one flourishing hotel and 15 public houses - more than enough for a town of 3,500 inhabitants. Scotland's new railway system, which might have brought us an influx of guests, had yet to reach the town. I insisted that ours should be a temperance hotel, which meant that we sold no alcohol. I wanted the atmosphere to be one of restful contemplation, and indeed it was: I had decided to learn Latin, and found the peace and quiet very beneficial. But our would-be clients obviously preferred the mayhem of a hot, rowdy tavern. In consequence, we hardly made any money at all.

Regretfully, Isabella and I realised that we were not destined to be hoteliers. We shut the hotel and went to live in Glasgow.

In those years of early married life, I tried many occupations but none of them turned out to be successful. The job that I disliked the most was selling insurance. I worked in lots of different places - Glasgow, Perth, Dundee, Edinburgh, Leicester - but the principles were the same. I had to knock on the doors of complete strangers and persuade them to take out insurance policies on their homes. Being a shy man of few words, it was totally against my nature. No wonder I started having pains in the head again! It was as much as I could do to pursue my new studies in philosophy. Things got even worse when Isabella became ill: I was beside myself with worry, and I left my job so that we could move closer to her sister. Mercifully, she recovered; and privately, I was thankful that I would never have to make another sales pitch!

Next, I got a job as a journalist. 'Commonwealth' was a weekly newspaper published in Glasgow, and it was all about social and political reform. Writing, of course, was something that I enjoyed doing... but all the time, my thoughts kept wandering back to the questions that puzzled me most, just as they did when I was a lad. How I wished I'd had a good education! But university lecture theatres and libraries were not available to people like me. I began to wonder how I could ever get inside one. I would give anything, just to be able to eavesdrop on a lecture. What with all the disappointments and setbacks of the last few years, I began to doubt whether things would ever start looking up for me.

And then I saw it. The advertisement that could change my life! The Andersonian College in Glasgow required a janitor. Duties would include cleaning and airing the classrooms, lighting fires, and ensuring that the doors were opened before a lecture. I sat down there and then to write my application. My awkward hand could scarcely move quickly enough to complete the letter! With every cell in my body, I desired that position. I dreamed of walking around that place of learning, with access to every book I could ever wish to read; I would devour all the latest scientific papers, discuss them with professors and students, and perhaps even write some contributions of my own. Of course, I'd have to carry a mop and bucket around. But how long would it take to wash a floor?

While I waited for a reply, the days were interminable. I wobbled between hope and despair, and then I learned that no fewer than 60 people had applied for the job. My spirits sank. How could I ever succeed? When the letter came, I could barely bring myself to open it... and then I couldn't believe my eyes. I was being offered the job!

What a joy it was to work at the Andersonian College! Everyone was so warm and welcoming. I enjoyed being the 'doorkeeper' who admitted students into lectures; I confess that many of them would turn up without an official ticket, but I ushered them in anyway. And then, the best privilege of all, I could close the doors and stand quietly at the back, listening in awestruck silence to the lecture. When it had finished, I would make my way to the library. Ah, the smell of those old books! The caress of the leather bindings, and the crackle of crisp pages! I would happily have spent the rest of my days in that marvellous place...

Needless to say, while I was working at the Andersonian College I absorbed information like a sponge. Scientists were discussing the evidence for an ice age in the Earth's distant past, and I was fascinated by the questions they raised. No one really understood what had plunged the Earth into an ice age, when ice sheets covered much of its surface. I read that it could be caused by a change in the Earth's orbit, so that it starts to cool down when it is further away from the Sun. I realised that there must be other factors involved, too: the tilt of the Earth on its axis, and the way in which ice sheets reflect the Sun's heat back into space.

I was thrilled when my theories about ice ages were published in the Philosophical Magazine, one of the oldest and most respected scientific journals. They caught the eye of Sir Archibald Geikie, who was the Director of the Scottish Geological Survey. Sir Archibald was impressed with my work and he was eager for me to join his office in Edinburgh as a resident surveyor. I pondered long and hard about this: I was reluctant to leave the Andersonian College, but the cold draughts in my lodgings were playing havoc with my health. In Edinburgh, I would be earning a better salary, and perhaps I could afford a warmer place to live. So I accepted, and within a short space of time Isabella and I were installed in a cosy little house in Morningside.

My duties at the Geological Survey office were relatively easy, and I enjoyed exploring the countryside in the company of Sir Archibald Geikie, looking at all kinds of rocks and formations in the landscape. We were puzzling over the processes of glaciation, when glaciers scoured the Earth and then - very gradually - melted, leaving behind all kinds of fascinating phenomena. It seemed to me that the evidence we were looking for was right beneath our feet, if we could but see it!

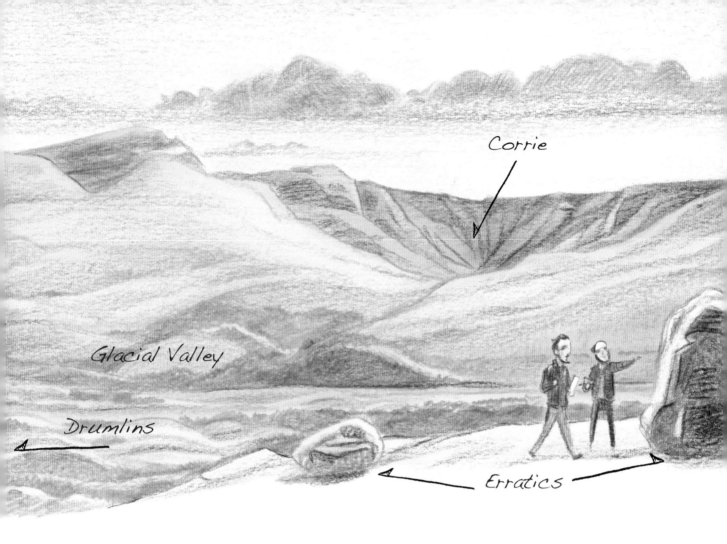

I set time aside for my own studies every evening. If the weather was fine, I would go out for a long walk, just to think. And if the weather was too bad for walking, my dear Isabella would always keep me company at home, bringing me cups of tea and reminding me that I did occasionally need to sleep...

This was a tiring, frustrating, yet exhilarating time. My head pains were growing worse, meaning that my speed of work had slowed right down. I was writing a book entitled 'Climate and Time in their Geological Relations', and I was corresponding with some of the most brilliant scientists in the world.

Sir Charles Darwin wrote to tell me how deeply interested he was in my theories, and consulted me about the ways in which ice ages might have developed. He was preparing a new edition of his famous book, 'On the Origin of Species', and was anxious to get his facts straight. What an honour that was!

With the geologist Sir Charles Lyell, I discussed the ways in which recurring changes in the Earth's orbit and tilt could affect its climate; and with the American scientist Louis Agassiz, I debated the direction of ocean currents and their impact on global temperatures. The famous botanist Sir Joseph Dalton Hooker corresponded with me at great length on many topics, including the possibility that the polar regions might, at one time, have been ice-free and warm enough to support plant life.

Much to my surprise, when my book was published I was contacted by a number of illustrious societies and institutions, all wishing to offer me an award. I was elected a Fellow of the Royal Society, and given an Honorary Doctorate by the University of St Andrews. The New York Academy of Sciences made me an Honorary Member. I could hardly believe that this was happening to the young lad who'd had hardly any education, who just happened to see a copy of the Penny Magazine in a shop window, and who had managed to teach himself pretty much everything he knew.

And so here I am, standing in front of this wonderful audience and preparing to deliver my lecture. As always, I am terribly nervous. Part of me still doubts whether my ideas are valid or interesting. Yet when I start speaking, my confidence returns because I love trying to explain the deepest mysteries of the universe. These are the questions that have inspired me all my life. Maybe, if you will allow your thoughts to soar into the vastness of space and time, you will find inspiration too.

Isabella is so proud of me. She knew all along, she says, that I was never meant to sell packets of Assam tea or to worry people about the risks of their house catching fire. She could see, apparently, that I was destined for bigger things. I owe all my success to her... and to my belief that a little bit of daydreaming will take you a very long way.

Towards the end of the last glacial period, which ended 11,700 years ago

Climate & Time
the Science of James Croll

The map of the Earth is quite familiar to us today, with ice sheets in the Arctic and the Antarctic, and large land masses known as continents surrounded by ocean. But if we could step back into the Earth's distant past, we would see that it once looked very different. At several times in the history of the Earth, most of its surface has been covered by thick ice sheets. These periods are known as ice ages. Over thousands and millions of years, the extent of the ice increased as the Earth cooled, and decreased as it gradually warmed. The times when the ice was increasing are called glacial periods, and the times when it was decreasing are called interglacial periods.

During the last glacial period, which ended around 11,700 years ago, woolly mammoths roamed the Earth, along with other animals that were adapted to survive in the cold conditions. Because most of the sea was frozen, the map of the British Isles looked very different; in fact, it was still joined to the land mass that is now Europe.

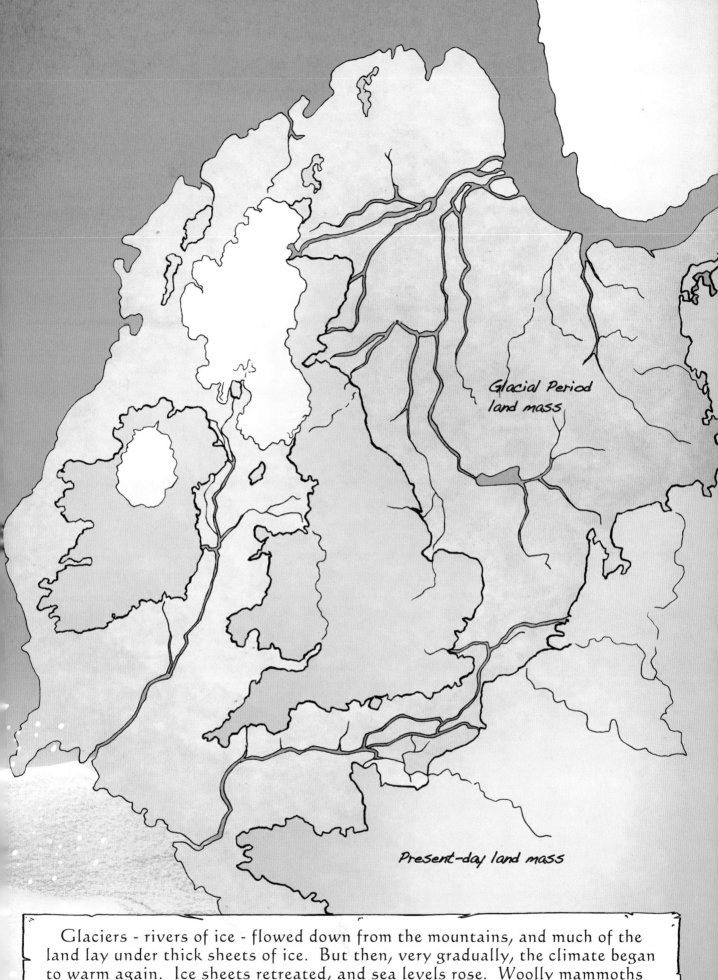

Glacial Period
land mass

Present-day land mass

Glaciers - rivers of ice - flowed down from the mountains, and much of the land lay under thick sheets of ice. But then, very gradually, the climate began to warm again. Ice sheets retreated, and sea levels rose. Woolly mammoths became extinct, while other animals flourished. Humans began to explore the newly exposed ground.

What caused these drastic changes in the Earth's climate? Let me explain...

Most of the planets rotate from west to east, but Venus and Saturn rotate from east to west.
The extreme tilt of Uranus makes it appear to spin on its side, orbiting the Sun like a rolling ball.

Uranus

Comet

Neptune

The Sun   Venus

Earth

Mercury.

Jupiter

Mars

Saturn

The Earth is one of eight planets in the solar system. They all revolve around the Sun, which is in fact a star. As you can see, the distance between the planets and the Sun varies dramatically, from Mercury, which is the closest, to Neptune, which is the farthest.

This distance has a great impact on the amount of heat and light that each planet receives.

We might assume that the amount of heat reaching the Earth from the Sun always stays the same, but in fact it changes very gradually over thousands of years. There are several reasons for this change:

(1) It takes a year for the Earth to make one complete orbit of the Sun. Over a period of 100,000 years, the Earth's orbit varies from nearly circular to slightly elliptical or egg-shaped. When it is closest to the Sun, it is 84 million miles away, and at its furthest point it is 96 million miles away. Scientists measure the 'eccentricity' of the Earth's orbit by calculating how much it differs from a perfect circle. At its furthest point, the Earth receives less heat from the Sun than it does at its closest point.

(2) The Earth is on a tilt in space: it doesn't sit on a perfect north-south alignment with the Sun, but instead it sits at an angle. Scientists call this 'obliquity'.

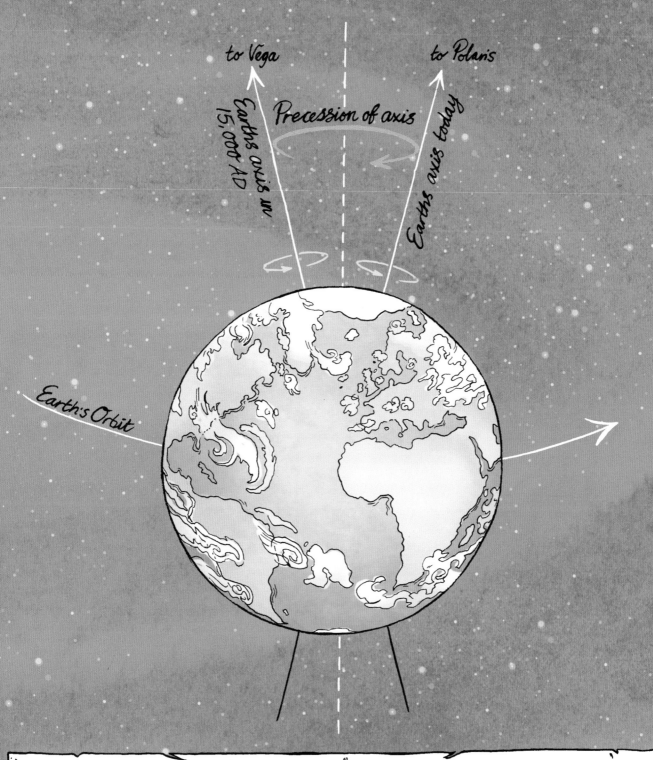

to Vega

to Polaris

Precession of axis

Earth's axis in 15,000 AD

Earth's axis today

Earth's Orbit

When the angle of tilt is greater, the Earth receives more heat. The angle of obliquity varies between 22 degrees and 25 degrees over a period of 41,000 years.

(3) The Earth's spin is what gives us day and night. We can imagine it spinning on an invisible axis, with the North Pole at the top and the South Pole at the bottom. But this spin isn't perfect. Imagine the Earth spinning like a basketball on your finger, and wobbling slightly as it spins. The amount of wobble in the Earth's spin varies over a period of 25,700 years. Scientists call this 'precession'.

These three processes can be shown as recurring and predictable patterns in the history of the Earth, and together they can dictate the beginning and end of ice ages.

Imagine that the Earth is at its furthest point from the Sun. This, together with its tilt and wobble, is causing the climate to cool down. Ice sheets are building up on land, and the oceans are starting to freeze.

Two things happen to make sure that the Earth continues to cool. Firstly, the ice sheets reflect much of the Sun's heat back into space; and secondly, with much of the sea frozen, the ocean currents can no longer bring warm water from the tropics to colder regions. These are called 'feedback mechanisms'. As a result, the ice sheets become so deep and widespread that they do not thaw, even in summer. The cooling of the Earth is now self-perpetuating. The stage is set for an ice age lasting many millions of years.

Using what we already knew about irregularities in the Earth's orbit, tilt and spin, and adding in my own theories about feedback mechanisms, I calculated a pattern of glacial periods extending hundreds of thousands of years into the Earth's past and hundreds of thousands of years into the future.

Ice Sheet

Earth's surface

Present

Timeline
of Discovery

It has taken many years for us to understand what causes the Earth's ice ages...

1833: Scientists who were puzzling over glacial features in the landscape believed that they were caused not by ice, but by Noah's great flood, as described in the Bible. Sir Charles Lyell proposed that the huge boulders known as 'erratics' were dropped by icebergs as they floated over submerged continents. In fact, erratics were simply big rocks trapped inside moving ice sheets and carried for many miles until the ice began to melt.

1837: Louis Agassiz was one of the first scientists to suggest that the Earth had experienced an ice age. He proposed that the entire northern hemisphere had once been covered by ice.

1864: James Croll published his theory on the causes of glacial periods. He was the first to combine four factors - eccentricity in the Earth's orbit, changes in tilt and spin, and feedback from ice sheets - in his calculations.

1894: The geologist Professor James Geikie, who was the younger brother of Sir Archibald, published glacial maps of North America, Europe and Asia.

1920s: A Serbian scientist, Milutin Milankovitch, built upon the theories of James Croll and other scientists to predict the occurrence of glacial periods. His calculations are known as Milankovitch Cycles (or Croll-Milankovitch cycles).

We now know that the Earth has experienced at least five major ice ages, and some of them lasted for hundreds of millions of years. During the last ice age - the Quaternary, which began about 2.5 million years ago - thick ice sheets expanded over much of the northern hemisphere and then shrank back again, in repeated cycles that lasted many thousands of years. Just as James Croll suggested, these cycles are caused by changes in the Earth's orbit, tilt and spin, together with the cooling effect of ice fields and changes in ocean circulation.

In the 1980s, carbon dioxide was recognised as another important factor affecting the Earth's climate. It was also acknowledged that humans had more impact on the climate than the Earth's orbit or any other factors. In fact, according to orbital theory, the Earth should be getting cooler, but human-made emissions of carbon dioxide from the burning of fossil fuels are now making it warmer. Since James Croll died in 1890, carbon dioxide levels have risen by nearly 50%.

Scientists continue to examine the causes and effects of climate change. In our understanding, we owe much to the brilliance of James Croll, one of the first climate scientists, who saw beyond his own human lifespan and pondered some of the deepest questions about climate and time.

Glossary

Axial tilt
Some planets rotate on an axis that is almost at right-angles to their orbital plane, while the axis of others is tilted. This is called axial tilt and it is measured in degrees. The Earth's axial tilt is 23.5 degrees.

Axis
An imaginary straight line around which a spinning object rotates. The Earth's axis extends from the North Pole to the South Pole through the centre of the Earth. The Earth rotates on its axis once every 24 hours.

Carbon dioxide
A colourless gas that occurs naturally in the Earth's atmosphere. It is comprised of one carbon atom and two oxygen atoms (CO_2).

Climate
The long-term prevailing weather conditions of a region, including air temperature, air pressure, wind, rainfall and sunshine. Climate is affected by many things including latitude, terrain, and height above sea level.

Climate change
A long-term shift in global or regional climate conditions

Eccentricity
The Earth's orbit around the Sun is eccentric, meaning that it is not perfectly circular. Over a period of about 100,000 years the Earth's orbit varies from nearly circular to elliptical or egg-shaped. Eccentricity measures how much the shape of Earth's orbit differs from a perfect circle.

Erratic
A large boulder that has been picked up and transported a significant distance by the movement of a glacier or ice sheet and then left behind when the ice has melted.

Feedback mechanism
A process that adds impetus to an existing trend of cooling (or warming) in the climate; for example, ice sheets reflecting the Sun's heat will accelerate the process of a cooling climate.

Geology
The study of the structure of the Earth, including its rocks and landforms, and the ways in which they have changed over time.

Glacial period (formerly glacial epoch)
A period of time within an ice age, often lasting thousands of years, that is marked by colder temperatures and advancing ice sheets. The last glacial period ended about 15,000 years ago.

Glacier
A glacier is a slow-moving 'river' of ice. Glaciers can form in high mountains, from snowfall that never thaws but instead becomes compacted into ice. Once the build-up of ice has reached a certain size it starts to flow downhill under its own weight.

Glaciology
The study of glaciers and ice sheets and their impact on the surface of the Earth.

Ice age
A period, often lasting millions of years, during which ice sheets have covered most or all of the Earth's surface. Within each ice age are glacial periods, during which the ice is expanding, and interglacial periods, which are intermittent warm periods. The Earth has experienced at least five major ice ages. We are currently in an interglacial period of the Quaternary ice age.

Ice sheet
A layer of ice covering a large area of the Earth's surface. The Earth's largest ice sheet covers the Antarctic continent.

Interglacial period
A period of time within an ice age, often lasting thousands of years, that is marked by warmer temperatures and retreating ice sheets.

Milankovitch cycles
In the early 1900s the Serbian geophysicist Milutin Milankovitch (Milanković), drew charts to calculate how changes in the Earth's movements can trigger ice ages. These changes, which are repeated over thousands of years, are called Milankovitch cycles. He based his calculations on the work of James Croll and other scientists.

Obliquity
The angle at which the Earth's axis of rotation is tilted as it travels around the Sun. Obliquity gives us our summer and winter, as the northern and southern hemispheres are tilted towards or away from the Sun. The angle of obliquity slowly increases or decreases in a cycle that spans about 41,000 years.

Orbit
The path of a celestial object, such as a planet, as it travels through space around a larger object, such as the Sun.

Orbital plane
When a planet orbits a star (in our case, the Sun), it traces an invisible line which may be roughly circular or elliptical. Imagine that this orbit is the outer edge of a disc, whose centre is the Sun. This is the planet's orbital plane.

Planet
A large natural body that orbits the Sun or another star and has been shaped by its own gravity into a sphere. Unlike stars, planets do not generate heat and light by nuclear fusion.

Precession
As Earth rotates, it wobbles slightly upon its axis, like a basketball or a spinning top that is spinning slightly off-centre. This wobble is caused by the gravitational influences of the Sun and Moon that cause Earth to bulge at the equator, affecting its rotation. The cycle of axial precession spans about 25,700 years.

Solar system
Our solar system consists of a central star (the Sun) and eight planets which orbit around it. It also includes other, smaller objects such as moons, asteroids and dust belts.

Star
A massive ball of gas that generates energy, including light, from nuclear fusion in its hot dense core.

Sun
The star at the centre of our solar system.

Jo Woolf FRSGS

Jo is Writer-in-Residence at the Royal Scottish Geographical Society. She has written a book about great explorers, entitled 'The Great Horizon - 50 Tales of Exploration', and she is a regular contributor to RSGS's newsletter, 'The Geographer'. As a writer about nature and history, she has also written books on the folklore of trees and birds.
www.thehazeltree.co.uk

Dylan Gibson

Dylan is a freelance illustrator who lives and works in Highland Perthshire. He enjoys spending his time outdoors exploring the countryside with his wife and dogs. His work includes illustrations for picture books, graphic novels and you can find more about his work at www.dylangibsonillustration.co.uk

Acknowledgements

For the invitation to tell this story, and for detailed insight into Croll's life and work, Dylan and Jo would like to thank Mike Robinson, Chief Executive of the Royal Scottish Geographical Society (RSGS).

Thanks to Professor Iain Stewart for casting an eye over the text, and to Colin Woolf for design, layout and preparation.

RSGS would like to thank the following for their generous support:

Dynamic Earth - dynamicearth.co.uk
Zero Waste Scotland - zerowastescotland.org.uk
Geological Society of Glasgow - geologyglasgow.org.uk
Edinburgh Geological Society - edinburghgeolsoc.org
Perth & Kinross Council - pkc.gov.uk
The Saltire Society - saltiresociety.org.uk
Quaternary Research Association - qra.org.uk
Perth & Kinross Heritage Trust - pkht.org.uk

In the publication of this book we'd like to acknowledge
the kind support of Ronald Guild
Geography teacher at Fettes College, and for many years
a member of RSGS Text Book Committee